YOU'RE YOU, CHARLIE BROWN

YOU'RE YOU, CHARLIE BROWN

A *PEANUTS* BOOK

by Charles M. Schulz

HOLT, RINEHART AND WINSTON
New York   Chicago   San Francisco

THAT'S HIS "HA-HA, YOU HAVE TO SHOVEL IT, AND I DON'T" DANCE!

SCHULZ

NICE GOING...IT TOOK THAT STONE FOUR THOUSAND YEARS TO GET TO SHORE, AND NOW YOU'VE THROWN IT BACK!

EVERYTHING I DO MAKES ME FEEL GUILTY..

HEY, EVERYBODY! LET'S PLAY "KING OF THE HILL"!

WHOEVER IS ON TOP WILL BE "KING," SEE, AND...

ALL RIGHT, LET'S PLAY "QUEEN OF THE HILL"

MY DAD LIKES TO HAVE ME COME DOWN TO THE BARBER SHOP, AND WAIT FOR HIM

NO MATTER HOW BUSY HE IS, EVEN IF THE SHOP IS FULL OF CUSTOMERS, HE ALWAYS STOPS TO SAY, "HI" TO ME...

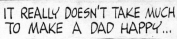

I SIT HERE ON THE BENCH UNTIL SIX O'CLOCK, WHEN HE'S THROUGH, AND THEN WE RIDE HOME TOGETHER..

IT REALLY DOESN'T TAKE MUCH TO MAKE A DAD HAPPY...

I CAN'T STAND THAT COMMERCIAL!

YOU CUT THAT OUT, YOU STUPID DOG!

WHY DON'T YOU GO SOME PLACE ELSE, AND SKATE?

YEAH, YOU'RE A NUISANCE! YOU AND YOUR FANCY FIGURES!

WHY DON'T YOU JUST GET OUT OF HERE?

GO ON! GET OUT OF HERE!

GET OUT OF HERE, AND LEAVE US ALONE!

SCHULZ

THE SUN IS GOING TO MELT YOUR SNOWMAN!

THE SUN IS GOING TO MELT YOUR SNOWMAN, AND ALL THAT WORK WILL BE FOR NOTHING! THE SUN IS GOING TO MELT YOUR SNOWMAN!

I SAID THE SUN IS GOING TO MELT THIS SNOWMAN!

STUPID SUN!!

CHARLIE BROWN, HOW DOES IT FEEL TO KNOW THAT YOU WILL NEVER BE A HERO?

WHAT MAKES YOU THINK I'LL NEVER BE A HERO? I MAY SURPRISE YOU! I MAY SAVE A LIFE OR REPORT A FIRE OR DO ALMOST ANYTHING!

LET ME PUT IT THIS WAY... HOW DOES IT FEEL WAY DOWN DEEP INSIDE IN YOUR VERY HEART OF HEARTS TO KNOW THAT YOU WILL NEVER BE A HERO?

TERRIBLE!

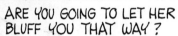

AND I GOT A VALENTINE FROM CLARA, AND I GOT ONE FROM VIRGINIA AND ONE FROM RUBY..

AND I GOT ONE FROM JOY, AND CÉCILE, AND JULIE, AND HEDY, AND JUNE, AND MARIE...

AND KATHLEEN, AND MAGGIE, AND DIANE, AND VIVIAN, AND CHARLOTTE, AND TEKLA, AND LILLIAN, AND...

GOOD GRIEF!

AND EDNA, AND NAOMI, AND LILA, AND FRAN, AND..

YOU DIDN'T GET A VALENTINE FROM LILA!

I DIDN'T? DIDN'T LILA SEND ME A VALENTINE?

LILA DOESN'T LOVE ME ANY MORE!

OH, WELL...AND CONNIE, AND CHIYO, AND MARILYN, AND AILEEN, AND..

I CAN'T STAND IT...I JUST CAN'T STAND IT....

I LOVE PLAYING HOCKEY BALL!

NOW HERE'S THE WAY WE START THE GAME..

WE HAVE A "FACE-OFF," SEE... WE LEAN OVER AND TAP OUR STICKS TOGETHER THREE TIMES.... OKAY, LET'S GO...

SMAK!

PENALTY BOX

POOF!

PICK A CARD... ANY CARD..

I'M DEPRESSED, LINUS...

I NEED AN ENCOURAGING WORD TO CHEER ME UP

HAPPINESS LIES IN OUR DESTINY LIKE A CLOUDLESS SKY BEFORE THE STORMS OF TOMORROW DESTROY THE DREAMS OF YESTERDAY AND LAST WEEK!

I THINK THAT BLANKET IS DOING SOMETHING TO YOU!

THE EASTER BUNNY IS OUT IN OUR FRONT YARD!

SURE, HE IS..

HE'S HIDING EGGS...HE'S DOING A SPRING DANCE, AND HE'S HIDING EGGS ALL OVER THE FRONT LAWN...

UH HUH... SURE, HE IS...

I THINK I'LL GO OUT AND GATHER UP ALL THE EGGS

WHY DON'T YOU JUST DO THAT...

YOU MISS A LOT WHEN YOU SIT AND WATCH TV ALL DAY LONG...

HERE'S THE WORLD FAMOUS GOLF-PRO RECEIVING HIS INVITATION TO PLAY IN THE MASTERS

AH, WHAT A THRILL!! GEORGIA IN THE SPRING!

I CAN SEE MYSELF NOW STANDING ON THE FIRST TEE...

ACTUALLY, BEAGLES ARE ALMOST NEVER INVITED TO PLAY IN THE MASTERS...

HERE'S THE WORLD FAMOUS GOLF PRO FLYING HIS PRIVATE JET TO AUGUSTA, GEORGIA!

HE HAS BEEN INVITED TO PLAY IN THE MASTERS GOLF TOURNAMENT..

I'VE NEVER BEEN TO AUGUSTA BEFORE...

I'LL PROBABLY STAY WITH ARNOLD AND WINNIE!

HERE'S THE WORLD FAMOUS GOLF PRO GOING OUT TO PLAY A PRACTICE ROUND AT THE MASTERS

I'LL PROBABLY PLAY WITH ARNIE TODAY, OR SAM, OR BEN, OR GAY'...

OF COURSE, THEY DON'T ALWAYS LIKE TO PLAY WITH ME...

THEY HATE IT WHEN I OUTDRIVE THEM!

HERE'S THE WORLD FAMOUS GOLF PRO TEEING OFF ON THE FIRST HOLE AT THE MASTERS...

AS HE WALKS DOWN THE FIRST FAIRWAY, HE IS FOLLOWED BY THAT HUGE THRONG OF HIS ADMIRERS KNOWN AS "SNOOPY'S SQUAD"

WINTER RULES ?

I THINK THERE'S SOMETHING WRONG WITH ME..

I KEEP HAVING THESE TINY SELF-DOUBTS...DO YOU THINK THIS IS WRONG?

OF COURSE, IT'S WRONG, CHARLIE BROWN...

I THINK YOU SHOULD HAVE GREAT-BIG SELF-DOUBTS!

I THOUGHT YOU WERE GOING TO STUDY FOR A HISTORY TEST..

I DON'T HAVE TO... I'M JUST GOING TO PUT THE BOOK UNDER MY PILLOW..

DURING THE NIGHT, THE ANSWERS WILL SEEP UPWARD THROUGH THE PILLOW AND INTO MY HEAD.....

I HOPE!

HAPPY FATHER'S DAY from your rare gem.

HI, ROY...I SUPPOSE YOU'RE WONDERING WHAT I'M DOING...

I'VE JUST MADE MY DAD A HAND-MADE FATHER'S DAY CARD..

EVERY NOW AND THEN MY DAD SAYS TO ME, "PEPPERMINT PATTY, DO YOU KNOW WHAT YOU ARE?" AND I ALWAYS SAY, "NO"...THEN HE SAYS TO ME, "YOU ARE A RARE GEM!" AND WE BOTH LAUGH...

SO YOU SEE, I'VE MADE A CARD FOR HIM... "HAPPY FATHER'S DAY FROM YOUR RARE GEM"

THAT'S VERY NICE..

THANK YOU..I'LL PUT IT ON TOP OF HIS DRESSER WHERE HE'LL SEE IT...

ACTUALLY, ANYONE WHO GIVES HIS DAD A FATHER'S DAY CARD IS A RARE GEM...

SCHROEDER, WHAT WOULD HAPPEN IF YOU AND I GOT MARRIED SOMEDAY, AND I GOT TIRED OF FIXING YOUR BREAKFAST?

I MEAN, WHAT WOULD HAPPEN IF I DECIDED I'D RATHER SLEEP IN THE MORNING?

I CAN'T STAND IT...

SAY, FOR INSTANCE, I GOT TIRED OF GETTING UP EVERY MORNING TO FIX YOUR BREAKFAST, AND JUST SUDDENLY DECIDED I'D RATHER SLEEP LATE EVERY MORNING...

I MEAN, WHAT WOULD YOUR REACTION BE?

ROWRR!!

WELL, PERHAPS I COULD SLEEP LATE ON WEEKENDS...

WATCH IT, BEAGLE!

SIGH

THERE'S ANOTHER GOOD THING ABOUT PLAYING NIGHT GAMES, CHARLIE BROWN..

SAY YOU'RE PITCHING A LOUSY GAME, SEE, AND WE WANT TO GET YOU OUT OF THERE...WELL, ALL WE HAVE TO DO IS COME OUT TO THE MOUND AND BLOW OUT YOUR CANDLE!

POOF!

I THINK WE'D BETTER STICK TO DAY GAMES!

I WAS WATCHING THIS BALL GAME ON TV LAST YEAR..

ONE OF THE PLAYERS GOT REAL MAD AT THE UMPIRE, AND KICKED DIRT ON HIM...

...LIKE THIS!

YOU CAN LEARN A LOT WATCHING THOSE GAMES ON TV!

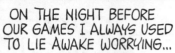

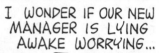

DANGER!
Kite-eating
tree

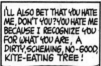

HELLO, YOU DIRTY KITE-EATING TREE! HAVE YOU HAD A HARD WINTER? I'LL BET YOU'RE HUNGRY, AREN'T YOU?

I'LL ALSO BET THAT YOU HATE ME, DON'T YOU? YOU HATE ME BECAUSE I RECOGNIZE YOU FOR WHAT YOU ARE, A DIRTY, SCHEMING, NO-GOOD, KITE-EATING TREE!

YOU ALSO HATE ME BECAUSE YOU NEED ME! I'M THE ONLY ONE AROUND HERE WHO FLIES KITES, AND WITHOUT ME, YOU'D GET PRETTY HUNGRY!

WHAT WOULD YOU DO IF I DECIDED NOT TO FLY ANY KITES THIS YEAR? WHAT WOULD YOU DO?

YOU'D STARVE TO DEATH, THAT'S WHAT YOU'D DO!

IT SORT OF SHAKES YOU UP, DOESN'T IT? WITHOUT ME, YOU'RE NOTHING!!

EXCUSE ME, CHARLIE BROWN, BUT YOU LOOK SORT OF DIFFERENT... LIKE SOME CHANGE HAS COME OVER YOU...

I THINK MAYBE IT HAS...

FOR THE FIRST TIME IN MY LIFE I FEEL NEEDED!

POW!

YOU HAVE CUTE TOES, CHARLIE BROWN!

THIS IS THE SAME THING I HAD TO EAT YESTERDAY..

IN FACT, THIS IS THE SAME THING I' HAD TO EAT EVERY DAY FOR THE PAST MONTH!

I THINK I'LL REGISTER A COMPLAINT...

AFTER I'VE FINISHED EATING!

DON'T YOU EVER GET TIRED OF THAT BLANKET?

NOT REALLY!

KLUNK!

KLUNK!

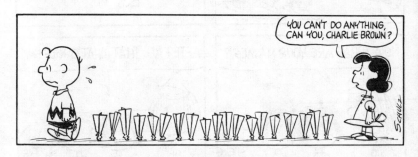

YOU CAN'T DO ANYTHING, CAN YOU, CHARLIE BROWN?

WELL, SO LONG, ROY... I'M OFF TO CAMP!

THIS YEAR I'M IN CHARGE OF A TENT... I'M ALMOST LIKE A COUNSELOR...ISN'T THAT GREAT?

I LOVE GOING TO CAMP..

FOR A GIRL LIKE ME, IT'S THE NEXT BEST THING TO BEING IN THE INFANTRY!

SCHULZ

HELLO, GIRLS... I'M "PEPPERMINT" PATTY, YOUR TENT MONITOR...

ACTUALLY, MY NAME REALLY ISN'T "PEPPERMINT" PATTY...THAT'S JUST A NICK-NAME MY DAD GAVE ME...HE ALSO CALLS ME HIS "RARE GEM"

NOW, WHAT ARE YOUR NAMES?

AFTER ALL THAT, WHAT CAN WE SAY?

"SOPHIE, CLARA AND SHIRLEY.."

NOW, LET'S SEE IF I HAVE YOU STRAIGHT..A GOOD TENT MONITOR MUST KNOW THE NAMES OF ALL THE GIRLS IN HER TENT..

YOU'RE SOPHIE, YOU'RE CLARA AND YOU'RE SHIRLEY.... RIGHT?

WRONG!

BUT THAT'S CLOSE ENOUGH.. WE'RE ONLY GONNA BE HERE FOR TWO WEEKS...

ALL RIGHT, GIRLS.. LIGHTS OUT!!

DID YOU ALL BRUSH YOUR TEETH?

WHAT IS THIS, A COMMERCIAL?

IS THIS YOUR BAT, CHARLIE BROWN? IT DOESN'T HAVE YOUR NAME ON IT...

YOU SHOULD HAVE YOUR NAME ON YOURS LIKE ALL OF THE BIG LEAGUE PLAYERS

LINUS HAS A WOOD-BURNING SET AT HOME... WHY DON'T I TAKE YOUR BAT, AND PUT YOUR NAME ON IT?

SAY! THIS IS GOING TO BE GREAT!

I'LL BE THE ONLY ONE AROUND HERE WITH HIS NAME ON A BAT!

THIS WILL REALLY IMPRESS THE KIDS ON THE OTHER TEAMS WE PLAY...THEY'LL BE AFRAID TO SEE ME STEP UP TO THE PLATE... THEY'LL THINK I'M A BIG-LEAGUER, AND I'LL...

HERE'S YOUR BAT, CHARLIE BROWN!

I HAD A LITTLE TROUBLE WITH THE WOOD-BURNING SET...

DID YOU SEE HOW I STRUCK OUT THAT LAST KID? PRETTY GOOD PITCHING, HUH?

YEAH, THAT WAS THAT KID WHO'S BEEN SICK IN BED ALL WINTER.. HIS DOCTOR SAYS HE'S GOING TO BE ALL RIGHT, BUT TO GET OUT IN THE SUN...

HE ALSO DOESN'T SEE VERY WELL, AND HE'S NEVER PLAYED BASEBALL BEFORE...

SOMETIMES A CATCHER CAN KNOW TOO MUCH ABOUT THE OPPOSITION...

POW!

..AND WE FOUND YOUR CAP OVER TWO BLOCKS AWAY, AND ONE OF YOUR SHOES THREE BLOCKS AWAY, AND ONE OF YOUR SOCKS TWO BLOCKS AWAY, AND..

ALL RIGHT!

CRACK!

CLOMP!

IN APPRECIATION OF THE GREAT PLAY YOU MADE THIS AFTERNOON, SNOOPY, THE TEAM HAS ASKED ME TO PRESENT YOU THIS...

HOW NICE...THE "GOLDEN MOUTH" AWARD!

AHEM!

Z

I HATE TO DISTURB YOU, BUT IF YOU'RE GOING TO SLEEP ON SECOND BASE, IT'S GOING TO PUT A LOT OF EXTRA PRESSURE ON ME AS PITCHER...

YOU SEE, I'LL HAVE TO TRY TO HOLD THEIR HITTERS TO SINGLES, AND I'M NOT SURE I CAN DO THAT...IF ONE OF THEIR HITTERS GETS TO ME FOR A DOUBLE OR A TRIPLE OR A HOME RUN, YOU KNOW WHAT'S GOING TO HAPPEN?

HE'S GONNA STOMP RIGHT ON YOUR STOMACH!!

THAT'S WHAT IS KNOWN AS MEANINGFUL DIALOGUE

I HAD FORGOTTEN THAT THIS WAS AN ELECTION YEAR...

HE'S A NICE GUY, BUT I DON'T KNOW WHERE HE STANDS...

THAT'S AN INTERESTING POINT OF VIEW...

THE ECONOMY CANDIDATE!

IT LOOKS LIKE A WIDE-OPEN CONVENTION!

AH!

I **KNEW** WE'D GET AROUND TO MY KIND OF CANDIDATE...

Panel 3 (row 2):
HOW SHALL WE PITCH THIS NEXT GUY, CHARLIE BROWN?

WELL, I DON'T KNOW..

THROW HIM YOUR CURVE, CHARLIE BROWN

SAY, HAVE YOU NOTICED HOW BUILT-UP IT'S GETTING AROUND HERE? PRETTY SOON THERE WON'T BE ANY PLACE FOR US TO PLAY..LOOK AT ALL THE HOUSES...

MY GRAMPA SAYS THAT ALL OF THIS USED TO BE A BIG PASTURE..

HE SAYS HE CAN REMEMBER WHEN THEY USED TO DRIVE CATTLE RIGHT ACROSS HERE

MY DAD SAYS HE COULD HAVE MADE A LOT OF MONEY IF HE HAD BOUGHT THIS LAND TWENTY YEARS AGO

TWENTY YEARS AGO? FIVE YEARS AGO WOULD HAVE BEEN ENOUGH!

THAT'S WHAT I SAY!

OF COURSE! LAND VALUES ARE GOING UP EVERYWHERE

LOOK AT THAT PLACE WHERE THEY PUT UP THE NEW SUPER-MARKET..

THAT'S WHAT MY GRAMPA WAS TALKING ABOUT. HE SAID YOU COULD HAVE BOUGHT THAT PROPERTY FOR ALMOST NOTHING ONLY TWO YEARS AGO!

WHAT DO YOU THINK, CHARLIE BROWN?

FRANKLY, I THINK HE'D HIT A CURVE BALL...

I'M GOING TO TELL YOU SOMETHING I'VE NEVER TOLD ANYONE BEFORE...

DO YOU SEE THAT HILL OVER THERE?

SOMEDAY, I'M GOING TO GO OVER THAT HILL, AND FIND THE ANSWER TO MY DREAMS...

SOMEDAY I'M GOING TO GO OVER THAT HILL, AND FIND HAPPINESS AND FULFILLMENT...

I THINK THAT, FOR ME, ALL THE ANSWERS TO LIFE LIE BEYOND THOSE CLOUDS AND OVER THE GRASSY SLOPES OF THAT HILL!

PERHAPS THERE'S ANOTHER LITTLE KID ON THE OTHER SIDE OF THAT HILL WHO IS LOOKING THIS WAY AND THINKING THAT ALL THE ANSWERS TO LIFE LIE ON THIS SIDE OF THAT HILL...

FORGET IT, KID!

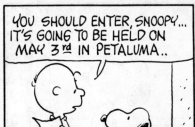

HERE'S THE WORLD-FAMOUS WRIST WRESTLER TAKING PART IN A PRACTICE MATCH BEFORE HE GOES TO PETALUMA FOR THE CHAMPIONSHIPS...

WAM!

THERE'S FEAR AND TREMBLING IN PETALUMA TONIGHT!

Schulz

KLUNK!!

WE WRIST WRESTLERS SHOW OUR OPPONENTS NO MERCY!

Schulz

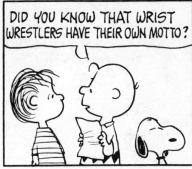

IT SEEMS AS IF WE'RE ALWAYS SAYING GOODBY, DOESN'T IT, SNOOPY?

ANYWAY, GOOD LUCK IN PETALUMA! BRING BACK THE WORLD'S WRIST WRESTLING CHAMPIONSHIP... I KNOW YOU CAN DO IT!

GOODBY, OL' PAL...

GOODBYS ALWAYS MAKE MY THROAT HURT... I NEED MORE HELLOS...

THAT STUPID BEAGLE HAS GONE TO **PETALUMA**?!

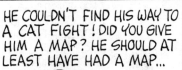

HE COULDN'T FIND HIS WAY TO A CAT FIGHT! DID YOU GIVE HIM A MAP? HE SHOULD AT LEAST HAVE HAD A MAP...

DID YOU GIVE HIM A MAP?

WELL, IT WASN'T EXACTLY A MAP.....

I HATE WINDY DAYS...

WIND IS VERY IMPORTANT... WITHOUT WIND OUR WORLD WOULD BE LIFELESS!

OUR OCEANS WOULD BECOME STAGNANT PONDS..CLOUDS WOULD NOT MOVE..FLAGS WOULD NOT FLY...

EARS WOULD NOT FLAP!

SCHULZ

I DON'T THINK MY TEACHER, MISS OTHMAR, LIKES ME ANY MORE..

SHE DOESN'T LOOK AT ME THE WAY SHE USED TO... SHE DOESN'T EVEN LOOK AT ME AT ALL...

IT'S A TERRIBLE THING TO DISCOVER THAT YOUR TEACHER DOESN'T LIKE YOU ANY MORE...

IT'S LIKE HAVING A SUBSCRIPTION RUN OUT..

SCHULZ

I LOVE MY SOPWITH CAMEL

HERE'S THE WORLD WAR I FLYING ACE WALKING OUT ONTO THE AERODROME AT REMBERCOURT...

THE MONTH IS OCTOBER.. THE YEAR, 1918!

I HAVE BEEN ASSIGNED TO A NIGHT-FIGHTER UNIT..

AS I CLIMB INTO THE SKY, THE HUGE Le Rhone ROTARY ENGINE IN MY SOPWITH CAMEL THROBS ITS SONG OF DESTINY

WE FLYING ACES ARE VERY DRAMATIC

MY MISSION IS TO FLY SOUTH FROM VERDUN TO ST. MIHIEL AND THEN SOUTHWEST TO BAR-LE-DUC, HOPING TO TRAP A GERMAN GOTHA BOMBER IN THE NIGHT...

THERE'S ONLY ONE THING WRONG...

BAM BAM BAM BAM

I'M AFRAID OF THE DARK!

SCHULZ

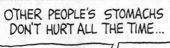

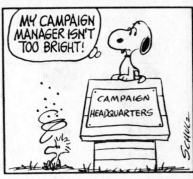

SCHULZ

THAT'S GOOD EXERCISE!

THAT'S NOT ART!

THAT'S A TERRIBLE DRAWING! YOU HAVE ABSOLUTELY NO TALENT!

NO ONE EVER LISTENS TO US CRITICS...

SIGH!

CURSE THIS STUPID WAR!

HERE'S THE WORLD WAR I FLYING ACE SITTING ON HIS BUNK...HE IS DEPRESSED..

THIS WAR IS NEVER GOING TO END..IT'S ALL MADNESS...IT'S INSANITY?!

I NEED SOMEONE TO TALK TO..

PERHAPS ONE OF THE NURSES AT THE DISPENSARY WILL TALK WITH ME....

WELL! I WAS WONDERING HOW LONG IT WOULD BE BEFORE YOU CAME TO SEE ME...

PSYCHIATRIC HELP 5¢

THE DOCTOR IS IN

AH! A DARK-HAIRED LASS... QUITE A BEAUTY, TOO! IT'S GOOD TO SEE A FEMININE FACE...

IT'S JUST NOT NORMAL FOR A BEAGLE TO GO AROUND WEARING A FLYING HELMET..

IT'S HEART-WARMING TO THINK OF THESE AMERICAN GIRLS COMING CLEAR OVER HERE TO SERVE!

SNIF

THE FIRST THING WE HAVE TO DO IS TALK ABOUT HOW ALL THIS STARTED..

I THINK THIS LASS HAS FALLEN FOR ME ALREADY.. THE NEXT MOVE IS OBVIOUSLY MINE........ SHOULD I OR SHOULDN'T I? WHO KNOWS WHAT TOMORROW MAY BRING?

SMAK

ALL SOLDIERS SHOULD KISS AN ARMY NURSE AT LEAST ONCE IN THEIR LIVES!

SCHULZ

I KNOW WHAT'S ON YOUR MIND...

LET ME WARN YOU RIGHT NOW THAT FOR EVERY SNOWBALL YOU THROW AT ME, I'M GOING TO CLOBBER YOU WITH **FIVE!**

WAP!

POW! POW! POW! POW! POW!

WAP!

POW! POW! POW! POW! POW!!

WAP!

POW! POW! POW! POW! POW!

WAP!

POW! POW! POW! POW! POW!!

THE ODDS ARE KILLING ME!

SCHULZ

I HATE WINDY DAYS!

HERE'S THE WORLD WAR I FLYING ACE OVER PONT-A-MOUSSON WITH THE EIGHTH U.S. AERO SQUADRON...

THE TIME IS 5:00 P.M. ON NOVEMBER 3, 1918... WE ARE TAKING PHOTOGRAPHS AT AN ALTITUDE OF 2200 METERS...

DOWN BELOW I CAN SEE THE POSITIONS OCCUPIED BY THE NINETY-SECOND U.S. ARMY DIVISION, AND TWO THOUSAND YARDS TO THE NORTH I CAN SEE THE GERMAN POSITIONS...

HAVE YOU EVER IN ALL YOUR LIFE SEEN SUCH GOOD RESEARCH?

PTUI!

I THOUGHT YOU WERE OUT THROWING SNOWBALLS..

NO, I WAS OUT **NOT** THROWING SNOWBALLS

SOMETIMES I DON'T UNDERSTAND YOU...

THERE ARE A LOT OF THINGS I DON'T UNDERSTAND MYSELF!

I MISS SKATING WITH SONJA HENIE...

HERE'S THE WORLD FAMOUS FIGURE SKATER PRACTICING HIS "OUTSIDE EIGHTS"

HE REALIZES THAT HE MUST PRACTICE DILIGENTLY IF HE IS TO WIN A GOLD MEDAL AT THE OLYMPICS...

ACTUALLY, VERY FEW BEAGLES ARE EVER INVITED TO THE OLYMPICS!

I'M TAKING UP A COLLECTION TO SEND SNOOPY TO THE OLYMPICS..

HOW MUCH DO YOU HAVE SO FAR?

EIGHTEEN CENTS

EIGHTEEN CENTS?! HOW IN THE WORLD IS HE GOING TO GET TO FRANCE ON EIGHTEEN CENTS?

DOES HE HAVE TO GO FIRST-CLASS?

I'M TAKING UP A COLLECTION TO SEND SNOOPY TO FRANCE TO SKATE IN THE OLYMPICS..

I DON'T SUPPOSE YOU'D CARE TO CONTRIBUTE?

SURE, I WOULD, BUT WHY STOP THERE? HERE'S A QUARTER... SEND HIM TO THE **MOON**!!

SILLY GIRL...SHE SHOULD KNOW THEY DON'T HAVE FIGURE SKATING ON THE MOON

STUPID BEAGLE!!

"GOODBY"? YOU'RE NOT SERIOUS?!

YOU'RE REALLY GOING TO FRANCE FOR THE OLYMPICS? I DON'T BELIEVE IT! THIS IS RIDICULOUS!!

BESIDES, THE OLYMPICS DON'T BEGIN UNTIL FEBRUARY! YOU'RE GOING TO MISS CHRISTMAS AND EVERYTHING! WHY DO YOU HAVE TO LEAVE **NOW**?

IT'S A LONG WALK!

THIS IS ALL YOUR FAULT! YOU WERE THE ONE WHO TOOK UP THAT **COLLECTION**!

NOW MY DOG HAS LEFT!! HE'S OFF SOMEWHERE WANDERING ACROSS THE COUNTRY! I'LL NEVER SEE HIM AGAIN! HE'S GONE!

BUT HE **WANTED** TO GO, CHARLIE BROWN! HE WANTED TO!

THAT'S RIDICULOUS! HE DOESN'T HAVE ANY IDEA WHAT HE'S DOING!

HERE'S THE WORLD-FAMOUS FIGURE SKATER ON HIS WAY TO FRANCE TO COMPETE IN THE OLYMPICS...

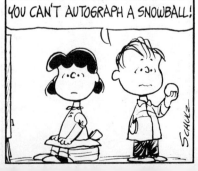

HOW NICE OF HIM...HE JUST FLEW IN FROM GRENOBLE, AND HE SAID I WOULD HAVE WON EASILY!